Josie and the Parade

Monica Hughes

Illustrated by Lisa Smith

"I want to see the parade."

"I want to see the horses."

"I want to see the flags."

"I want to see the jugglers."

"I want to see the band."

"I want to see the clowns."

"Dad! I **want** to see the parade!"

15

"Dad! I **can** see the parade!"